Snuggle Up, Sleepy Ones

For Marion, fellow author and friend
~ C. F.

For my nephew, Jamie Wernert
~ T. M.

ISBN 0-439-82918-6

Copyright © 2005 by Good Books, Intercourse, PA 17534.
Text copyright © 2004 by Claire Freedman. Illustrations
copyright © 2004 by Tina Macnaughton. All rights reserved.
Published by Scholastic Inc., 557 Broadway, New York, NY 10012,
by arrangement with Good Books. SCHOLASTIC and associated
logos are trademarks and/or registered trademarks of Scholastic Inc.

12 11 10 9 8 7 6 5 4 3   5 6 7 8 9 10/0

Printed in the U.S.A.   40

First Scholastic printing, December 2005

Snuggle Up, Sleepy Ones

Claire Freedman   Tina Macnaughton

SCHOLASTIC INC.

New York Toronto London Auckland Sydney
Mexico City New Delhi Hong Kong Buenos Aires

The sun paints the sky
a warm, glowing red.
It's time to stop playing,
it's time for bed.

In the soft swampy mud,
baby hippo, so snug,
Cuddles up close
for a big hippo hug.

Through wild, waving grasses
shy antelope roam.

It's been a long day,
they're ready for home.

Bold leopard cubs rest
from practicing roars.
They snuggle together,
all tired, tangled paws.

While up in the treetops
birds twitter and cheep,

Until quieter and quieter,
they fall fast asleep.

Below in their nests
baby porcupines all
Curl up, snug and tight,
in one spiky ball.

With tired, drooping necks
giraffes flop to the ground.
Sheltered and watched over,
safe and sound.

And mischievous monkeys
shout down from the trees,
"It's not really dark yet.
Five more minutes, please!"

Zebras lie panting,
tired out from their play.
They sink into sleep
as the sun slips away.

Moths go by fluttering,
bats flitter by.
Elephants rumble
their deep lullaby.

Shadows grow deeper,
the lion cubs doze.
Drowsy heads nod,
little eyes start to close.

Stars twinkle brightly,
the moon softly gleams.
Snuggle up, sleepy ones.
Hush now, sweet dreams!

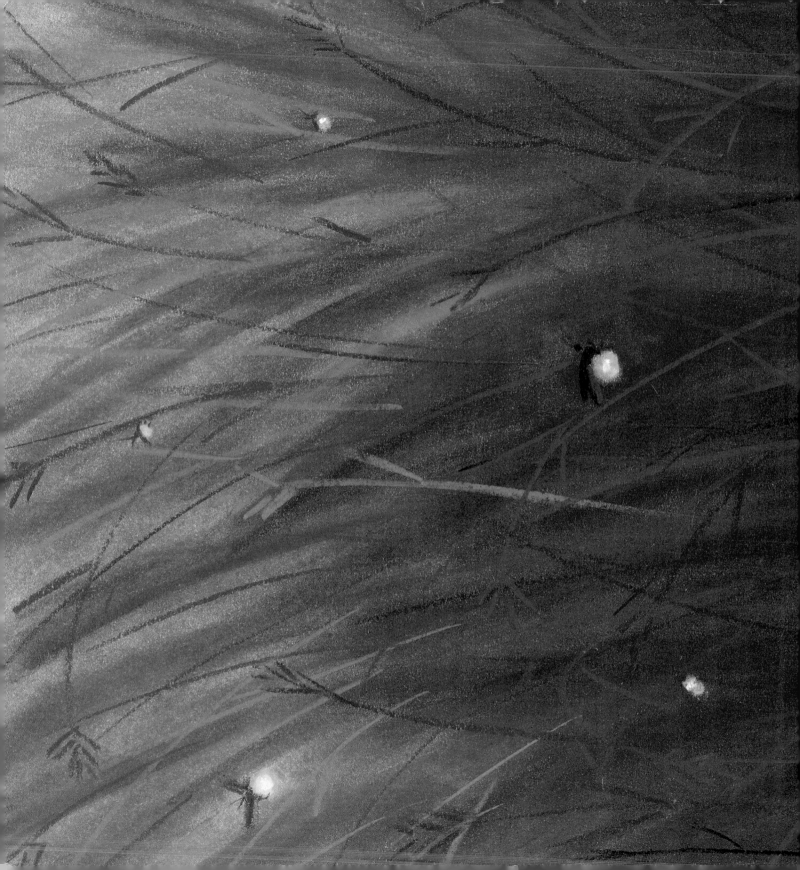

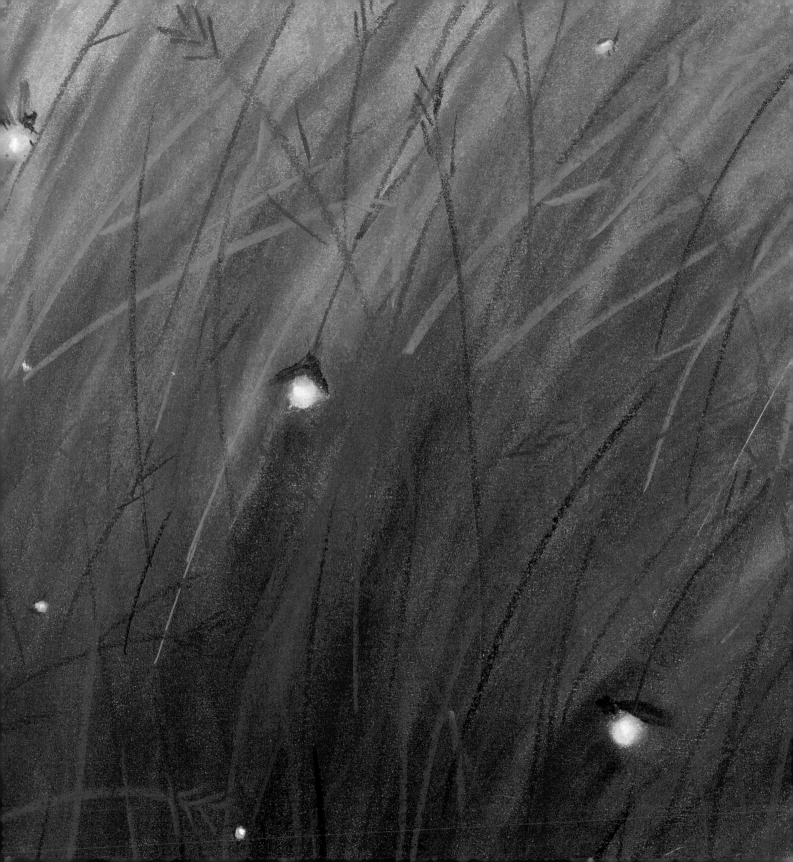